Contents

Words and sentences

Remember

When you write, you put **words** in order so they make a **sentence**.
A sentence makes sense and tells you something.

Jack went to the party.

Try it

1 Do the words make a **sentence**? Put a tick or cross in each box.

Lily sisters ☐   like books ☐

Lily has three sisters. ☐   rain wet ☐

I like books. ☐   Rain is wet. ☐

2 Look at the picture. Write a **word** on each line to complete
the sentence.

The _____ has a kite.

The boy rides his _____ .

The _____ hides by the tree.

The kite is in _____ sky.

The bird is _____ the tree.

Remember

Leave spaces between the **words** when you write a **sentence**.

Iwentforarun. ✗
I went for a run. ✓

More practice

1 Put the **words** in order so they make a **sentence**. Write each sentence with spaces between the words.

sad. was Ben   _____

have a I dog.   _____

sat Gran in chair. her   _____

the I to zoo. went   _____

the swim in Fish sea.   _____

2 Complete the **sentences** using your own **words**.

I like to _____ .

I have _____ .

I can _____ .

I go to _____ .

Today it is _____ .

Sentence practice

Complete this sentence.

The bus _____ .

Capital letters and full stops

Remember

A **sentence** must start with a **capital letter** and end with a **full stop**.

The little man ran away.

Try it

1 Does the sentence have a **capital letter** at the start and a **full stop** at the end? Put a tick or cross in each box.

it is hot today. ☐

The ducks began to quack ☐

A van went up the hill. ☐

My coat is blue. ☐

there are seven days in a week ☐

We like to paint. ☐

2 Write each **sentence** so it starts with a **capital letter** and ends with a **full stop**.

a dog can bark _____

we need food to eat _____

you can play here _____

the man was rich _____

it is cold today _____

my mum made a cake _____

Remember

When you write a **sentence**, put a **capital letter** at the start and a **full stop** at the end.

More practice

1 Look at the picture and write the start of each **sentence**. Remember to start with a **capital letter**.

_____ is pecking corn. _____ are eating grass.

_____ is by the gate. _____ has a bucket.

2 Write the end of each **sentence**. Remember to end with a **full stop**.

Starfish live in _____

A bird is singing in _____

The sun is _____

You can go sailing in _____

Sentence practice

Write a sentence about a bike. Remember the **capital letter** and **full stop**.

_____

Capital letters: names and 'I'

Remember

Always put a **capital letter** at the start of someone's name.

Beth played football with Joe and Evie.

Try it

1 Circle the **capital letter** at the start of every name you can see.

Sam has a dog called Benny.

Tanya plays ball with Ella.

Harry and Chris go to Adam's party.

Marlon likes to read with his friend James.

One day Poppy went to visit Nisha.

2 Look at the pictures. Add a name to complete each caption. Remember the **capital letter**.

my dog _____

my cat _____

This is _____ .

my friend _____

Remember

You use the word 'I' to write about yourself.
The word 'I' is always a **capital letter**.

Alex and I played football with
Vikram and Jodie.

More practice

1 Underline the words that need a **capital letter**. Then write each sentence correctly.

i think i can do it. _____

dad said i can help. _____

i went to see emma. _____

ellie and i saw jake. _____

now i must find luke. _____

2 Complete each sentence. Use a name or the word 'I'. Remember the **capital letter**.

_____ is my best friend.

_____ can run fast.

Simon and _____ like playing pirates.

I sit next to _____ .

This morning _____ was late for school.

Sentence practice

Write a sentence that needs <u>two</u> **capital letters** in it.

_____

9

Making up sentences

Remember

When you write, you put your ideas into **sentences**. It helps to say the sentence aloud before you write it.

I like to play on the swings.

Try it

1   Add some **words** to make these words into a **sentence**. Say each sentence, then write it.

mum shopping   _____

we play garden   _____

boy sand   _____

house green door   _____

fox den   _____

2   Look at the picture. Write <u>three</u> **sentences** about it. Say each sentence before you write it.

_____

_____

Remember

When you finish writing a **sentence**, read it. Check it makes sense and is complete.

More practice

1 Read each **sentence**. Put a tick in the box if the sentence makes sense and is complete. Put a cross if there is something missing.

Mum broke a cup. ☐

Jenny gave me a present ☐

The boys play with car. ☐

I saw a bee a flower. ☐

Molly came to play. ☐

The girl put her red shoes. ☐

2 Complete each **sentence**.

I like to _____

I want to _____

Today I saw _____

My house _____

Some dogs _____

Sentence practice

Write a sentence with these <u>two</u> **words** in it.

truck   road

_____

Using 'and' to join words

The word '**and**' is a **joining word**. You can use 'and' to join **words** together.

shops and houses   yellow and green

Try it

1   Use the word '**and**' to join these words together.

jelly _____ ice cream   girl _____ boy

Mum _____ Dad   hot _____ cold

bread _____ butter   hide _____ seek

arms _____ legs   you _____ me

2   Look at the picture. Complete the sentence, using '**and**' to join on another **word**.

It is hot _____

Dad eats fish _____

The girls play bat _____

Owen has a bucket _____

Dad took off his shoes _____

Remember

You can use 'and' to join words in a **sentence**.

He painted the shops and
houses yellow and green.
People stopped and stared.

More practice

1 The word 'and' is missing from these sentences. Write each
sentence correctly.

Let us wait see. _____

He began to huff puff. _____

They ran ran. _____

Rabbits can hop jump. _____

He sat down cried. _____

2 Complete the sentence using 'and' and another **word** or words.

Josie has a brother _____

He jumped up _____

Today it is cold _____

The woman put on her hat _____

The farmer fed the sheep _____

The flowers are red _____

Sentence practice

Write a sentence about <u>two</u> things you can see right now. Use
the word '**and**' in your sentence.

_____

Revision 1

1 Put the **words** in order so they make a **sentence**.

is kitchen. in Dad the _____

rocks. hit the ship The _____

car I outside. saw a _____

2 Check these **sentences**. Put a tick in the box if the sentence makes sense and is complete. Put a cross if there is something missing.

We slept in a tent. ☐

I need a pen ☐

I like to read a good book. ☐

the stars shine at night. ☐

3 Write these **sentences** correctly.

a scarf is made from wool _____

the Man was in a rush _____

4 There is a **word** missing from each **sentence**. Write the sentence correctly.

Dan has pet rabbit. _____

In winter it cold. _____

I see my brother sister. _____

5 Underline <u>three</u> **words** that need a **capital letter**. Write the words correctly.

Today i played with lily and brett.

_____   _____   _____

6 Complete each **sentence** using <u>two</u> food ideas from the picture. Join your two words with '**and**'.

We grew _____

I like _____

The shop sells _____

Dad needs _____

Writing task 1

My friend

Write about one of your friends. Your task is to say which friend it is, what you do together and why you are friends.

Before you start writing, think about:

- which friend you will write about

- what you like to do together

- why you are friends

Remember

- Write in sentences.
- Use full stops and capital letters.
- Check your work.

My friend

_____

_____

_____

_____

_____

_____

Draw a picture of you and your friend.

Using 'and' to join sentences

Remember

You can use the word '**and**' to join two **sentences** together.

Leah had a kite. She flew it in the park.   (2 sentences)

Leah had a kite and she flew it in the park.   (1 sentence)

Try it

1   Use the word '**and**' to join the two **sentences** together.
Read each new sentence you make.

Amir fell over _____ he hurt his leg.

Tom ran away _____ he hid outside.

Molly went to bed _____ she fell asleep.

We went to the park _____ I played on the swings.

Max took his net _____ he went fishing.

I like cats _____ I like dogs.

2   Complete each **sentence** with your own **word** or words.

The man gets in the car and he goes _____

Mum has coffee and I have _____

I put on my coat and I go _____

We went to the zoo and we saw _____

The sun is out and it _____

Remember

When you use the word 'and' to make one longer **sentence**, the sentence has a **capital letter** at the start and a **full stop** at the end.

The kite flew away and it landed in the tree.

More practice

1 Use the word **'and'** to join the two sentences. Write each new longer **sentence**.

Marie sat in the chair. She started to cry.

_____

The boy lay on his back. He looked at the clouds.

_____

Lucy saw a spider. She ran away.

_____

2 Write a **sentence** about each picture.

_____   _____

Now join the two sentences together using **'and'**.

_____

Sentence practice

Write a sentence about <u>two</u> things you did this morning. Use the word **'and'**.

_____

More capital letters

Remember

Capital letters are used at the start of place names, as well as people's names.

Maisie went shopping in London.

Try it

1 Circle the **capital letter** at the start of any names you can see.

Kate went to Spain for a week.

Omar took the bus to Chester.

Last week Nur drove to Wales.

We think Holly lives in Park Lane.

Liz met Mrs Scott on the corner of Bright Street.

2 Copy the sentence and add the **capital letters** at the start of any names.

ross lives in manchester.

yasmin went to cardiff.

vishal has a map of liverpool.

mr brown is in scotland.

adam ran down marsh lane.

Remember

The days of the week and the months of the year always start with
a **capital letter**.

On Saturday, Maisie went shopping.

More practice

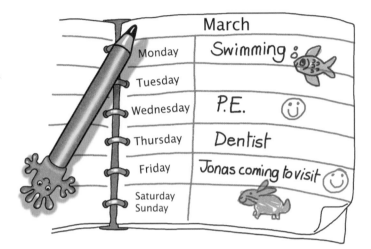

1 Look at Megan's calendar.
Complete each sentence
by adding the correct
day of the week.

Megan has the dentist on _____ .

She goes swimming on _____ .

Jonas is coming on _____ .

Megan has P.E. on _____ .

2 Complete these sentences by adding a place name, a day of the
week or a month of the year.

Today it is _____ .

We do art on _____ .

I live in _____ .

On _____ we go shopping in _____ .

My birthday is in _____ .

Sentence practice

Write a sentence with a person's name and a place name in it.

_____

Adding –s and –es

Remember

You add **–s** to the end of a **word** to show there is more than one of something. This makes a **plural**. 'Plural' means more than one.

one dog   (singular)   two dogs   (plural)

Try it

1 Add **–s** to make each word into a **plural**.

pen_____   pencil_____   ruler_____   desk_____   book_____

teacher_____   crayon_____   boy_____   tray_____   girl_____

2 Look at the picture. For each object, write how many you can see. One has been done for you.

bowl   _____two bowls_____   spoon   _____

teapot   _____   cup   _____

fork   _____   plate   _____

Remember

If a **word** ends in –ch, –sh, –s, –x
or –z, add **–es** to make a **plural**.

one fox   (singular)   two foxes   (plural)

More practice

1   Add **–s** or **–es** to make each word into a **plural**.
Write the plural word.

bag and box   _____ and _____

brush and broom   _____ and _____

witch and wizard   _____ and _____

skirt and dress   _____ and _____

tree and bush   _____ and _____

2   Add **–s** or **–es** to make one word into a **plural**. Then write each
sentence correctly.

This hen has six chick.   _____

She gave me three wish.   _____

Rabbits live in hutch.   _____

I like fish and chip.   _____

We all clap our hand.   _____

Sentence practice

Write a sentence with the **plurals** of these <u>two</u> **words** in it.

car   bus

_____

Question marks

Remember

A sentence that asks something is called a **question**.
A question ends with a **question mark**.

Where have you been?
What did you see?
Who did you meet?

Try it

1 Read each question. Put a **question mark** at the end of it.

Where did you go_____

Who did you meet_____

How did you feel_____

Why did you go out_____

When did you get back_____

Did you feel sad_____

2 Put the words in order so they make a **question**. Write each
question with a **question mark** at the end.

hid box the Who   _____

is Where hat my   _____

the bus come When will   _____

can What you see   _____

the ship How sink did   _____

> ## Remember
>
> All **sentences** start with a **capital letter**. Most sentences end with a **full stop**. **Questions** end with a **question mark**.

More practice

1 Read each sentence. Put a **full stop** or a **question mark** at the end.

Why did that happen____   It was cold in the garden____

We went to the coast____   Can you swim____

What did you do at school____   There is a frog in the pond____

2 Write <u>four</u> **questions** to ask the man in the picture.

What _____

Why _____

Where _____

_____

Sentence practice

There is a new child in your class. Write a **question** to ask him or her.

_____

25

Verb endings

Remember

Some words tell you what people are doing. 'Doing words' are also called **verbs**. You can add the **word endings** –ing, –ed, –s and –er on to the end of verbs.

play   playing   played   plays   player

Try it

1 Add the **endings** to the end of these verbs. Write each new **word**.

clean + ing = _____   clean + er = _____

sing + er = _____   sing + ing = _____

push + ing = _____   push + ed = _____

wait + ed = _____   wait + er = _____

float + s = _____   float + ing = _____

2 Underline each **word** with the ending –ed, –ing, –s or –er.

The painter painted the door red.

Jenny helps with washing the car.

Mum is cooking stew and I am watching.

The football player played his best game.

She looked at the frog and sighed.

The starter starts the race.

Remember

You can use **verbs** in different ways when you add **word endings** to them.

The banjo play*er* likes play*ing* the banjo.

More practice

1 Add the **endings –er** and **–ing** so the sentences make sense.

Zack was play____ on his scoot____ .

The sing____ likes sing____ sad songs.

Dad put the fry____ pan on the cook____ .

The road sweep____ is sweep____ up the rubbish.

2 Look at the picture. Complete the **sentences** to say what everyone is doing. Use words with the **ending –ing**.

Lucas

Alex

Poppy

Alex _____

Lucas _____

Poppy _____

The teacher _____

Sentence practice

Add the **endings –ing** and **–er** to the word '**print**'. Then use the <u>two</u> new **words** in a sentence.

Revision 2

1 Something is missing from the end of each **sentence**. Write it in.

Where is the car____

The van went up the hill____

When will you get home____

I get the bus to school____

Did you see a blue truck____

A bike has two wheels____

2 There is a missing **word** in each **sentence**. Write the sentence correctly.

We saw the cows sheep.

_____

They sang for the king queen.

_____

I like looking books.

_____

3 Read the start of the story. Put in the missing **capital letters** and **full stops**.

once there was a girl called Ruby she had lots of money

4 Write these two sentences as <u>one</u> **sentence** using the word '**and**'.

Mum broke a cup. She was sad.

_____

5 Underline <u>two</u> **words** in the sentence that need to start with a **capital letter**. Then write the words correctly.

We saw ella and alfie on the beach.

_____ _____

Mr jones took us to belfast.

_____ _____

On monday i went to town.

_____ _____

In march I will go to italy.

_____ _____

6 Look at the picture. Write how many of each object you can see. One has been done for you.

mask _____three masks_____   button _____

bead _____   brush _____

card _____   crayon _____

Writing task 2

My party invitation

Write an invitation to a party. Choose an idea from the picture or use one of your own. Your task is to tell someone about the party and ask them to come.

Before you start writing, think about:

- who to invite

- when and where the party will be

- what to tell them about the party

Remember

- Write in sentences.
- Use full stops and capital letters.
- Check your work.

My party invitation

_____

_____

_____

_____

_____

_____

_____

Now decorate the border of your invitation.

Exclamation marks

Some sentences end with an **exclamation mark**. The exclamation mark tells you to read the sentence with strong feeling or in a loud voice.

Don't eat me!   Stop!   Come back at once!

Try it

1 Put an **exclamation mark** at the end of the sentence. Then read it aloud with feeling.

Wait for me____   I want my mummy____

You are so funny____   I'm six today____

Leave me alone____   Don't be silly____

2 Look at the picture. Write these words in the bubbles to show the different feelings. Remember to use an **exclamation mark**.

Splash   Help   Shoo   Oops   Boo

Remember

Most sentences end with a **full stop**.
Only use an **exclamation mark** if the
sentence tells the reader something
surprising or exciting.

The gingerbread man jumped out of the oven!

More practice

1   Read the sentences. Put an **exclamation mark** at the end of
<u>three</u> sentences. End the other <u>two</u> sentences with a **full stop**.

The grass was made of jelly_____

I am going home_____

Bob fell in the pond_____

The man walked down the path_____

We found an elephant in the garden_____

2   Put the words in order so that they make a sentence that can
end with an **exclamation mark**.

my It is today birthday   _____

I a you surprise for have   _____

there right Stop   _____

went The pop balloon   _____

Sentence practice

Complete this sentence so that it ends with an **exclamation
mark**.

You are _____

Writing in sentences

Remember

When you write, you break your ideas up into a number of **sentences**. Each sentence starts with a **capital letter** and ends with a **full stop**.

Jamie went on holiday. He went camping with his family. They played on the beach and swam in the sea.

Try it

1 Read the two sentences on each line. Then add a **sentence** of your own.

It rained all day on Monday. The children had to stay inside.

_____

Bill was in a rowing boat. The boat started to fill with water.

_____

Alice went to the beach. She went for a swim in the sea.

_____

I saw a frog in the long grass. It was green with big eyes.

_____

2 Here are <u>three</u> **sentences**. They have no **capital letters** or **full stops**. Write them correctly.

the boy had a toy car he pushed it down the hill it went fast and crashed into a tree

_____

_____

Remember

Say your sentence. Write it. Then read it. Check that it makes sense and has the correct **punctuation**.

More practice

1 Read these three **sentences** carefully. Check that they make sense. Write them correctly.

Mum put the cake the oven. She went outside water the plants. She forgot about the cake it burnt.

_____

_____

_____

2 Write <u>three</u> **sentences** about the picture. Say each sentence, write it and then check it.

_____

_____

_____

_____

Sentence practice

Write <u>three</u> sentences about finding a caterpillar.

_____

_____

_____

Linking sentences

Remember

Sometimes you write sentences about a series of events. Start the sentences with **linking words** to show the order of events.

The little goat ran away from the farmyard. First he saw the farm cat sleeping by the gate. Then he saw three ducks quacking.

Try it

1 Underline any **linking words** at the start of a sentence.

Dad washed the car. Later he drove to town.

Hayden put on his coat. Then he put on his hat and scarf.

Kelly found some leaves. Next she found some seeds.

Isabelle went to bed. Soon she was fast asleep.

Jake was playing. Suddenly a big dog barked at him.

2 Add a **linking word** to start the second sentence on each line.

I went on the swings. _____ I went on the slide.

Oliver went into the woods. _____ he was lost.

Sunil was digging a hole. _____ she found a gold coin.

Simeon had a wash. _____ he brushed his teeth.

We played on the beach all morning. _____ we went in the sea.

Remember

You can use **linking words** to help you write stories or to write about things that happen.

More practice

1 Write the missing **sentences** to say what happened. Start your sentences with a **linking word**.

1.

We went for a picnic.

2.

_____

3.

We stood under a tree.

4.

_____

_____

2 Complete the **sentences** to say what the children did at the zoo.

First _____

Then _____

Next _____

Finally _____

Sentence practice

Write the next <u>two</u> sentences to say what happened. Start both your sentences with a **linking word**.

We went to the shops. _____

Describing words

Remember

You can add **describing words** to a sentence to give more detail.

The hen met a fox.
The little hen met a big fox.

Try it

1 Underline the **describing word** in each sentence.

I put on my green shorts.

There was a big spider in the bath.

Rose found a magic shell.

Leo is wearing a fluffy jumper.

I need a cold drink.

2 Add a **describing word** to each sentence to give more detail.

I like _____ apples best.

Lizzy found a _____ coin.

The moth had _____ wings.

I like a _____ pillow to sleep on.

We saw the _____ bull in the field.

Cinderella had two _____ sisters.

Remember

You can use two **describing words** together to make your sentences more interesting.

The hen met a fox.
The little brown hen met a thin red fox.

More practice

1 Write each sentence with <u>two</u> extra **describing words**.

The kitten was stuck in a tree.

_____

A girl ran into the woods.

_____

2 Look at the picture. Write <u>three</u> **sentences** about what the girl is wearing. Use all of the **describing words** below.

warm   thick   long   woolly   black   smart

_____

_____

_____

_____

Sentence practice

Write a sentence about a mouse. Use <u>two</u> **describing words** in your sentence.

_____

Adding un–

Remember

If you add the letters **un–** to the start of a **describing word** it makes a word that means the opposite.

lucky   unlucky

Try it

1 Add **un–** to the **describing word** to make a word that means the opposite.

Tilly was _____kind to me.   The rules are _____fair.

The story was _____true.   The king was _____wise to trust you.

2 Add **un–** to the **describing word** to make a word that matches the next picture.

happy   tidy   fit

_____   _____   _____

Remember

Sometimes you add **un–** to a **doing word** (or **verb**).
It changes the word like this:

I tie my laces. Then I untie them.

More practice

1 Add **un–** to these **doing words** or **verbs**.

_____cover _____fold _____dress _____curl

_____roll _____bolt _____pick _____zip

2 Add **un–** to the **verb** in **bold**. Write each new **sentence**.

This key will **lock** the door.

_____

I helped Jacob **pack** his bag.

_____

Max can **do** the zip on his jacket.

_____

The helpers will **load** the van.

_____

Sentence practice

Add **un–** to the **verb** below. Write a sentence using the new **word**.

block

_____

Revision 3

1 Write the two sentences as <u>one</u> **sentence**.

We played snakes and ladders. I won.

_____

Bella went to the park. She played on her bike.

_____

2 Write the missing **punctuation mark** at the end of each speech bubble.

3 Underline the **words** that need a **capital letter**.

Then hansel and gretel got lost in the wood.

We went to blackpool last saturday.

Mum said i should tell mr jackson.

My school is on blake street.

4 You can add **un–** to <u>three</u> of these **words**. Underline the three words.

rude   selfish   tidy   soft   good   kind

Now write the three words with un–.

_____   _____   _____

5 Add the correct **endings** to the **words** in **bold**.

Mrs Black is my **teach**_____.

She is **teach**_____ us about plants and flowers.

Yesterday she **show**_____ us a sunflower.

Today we are **learn**_____ about seeds.

6 Rewrite each **sentence**, adding in <u>two</u> **describing words**.

The man sat on the bench.

_____

The elephant spoke to the fly.

_____

The boy played with the kitten.

_____

Writing task 3

My day out

Write about a visit you have been on. Choose an idea from the picture or use one of your own. Your task is to tell someone about where you went and what you did.

Before you start writing, think about:

- where you went

- what you saw

- what you did

Remember

- Write in sentences.
- Use correct punctuation.
- Check your work.

My day out

_____

_____

_____

_____

_____

_____

_____

_____

_____

Draw a picture to show where you went.

Progress chart

Tick the circle when you can do what the statement says.

Section 1

◯ I can put words in order so that they make a sentence.

◯ I can leave spaces between my words when I write a sentence.

◯ I can write a sentence with a capital letter and a full stop.

◯ I can use a capital letter for people's names and the word 'I'.

◯ I can say a sentence, write it and check it.

◯ I can use the word 'and' to join words.

Section 2

◯ I can use 'and' to join two sentences together in one longer sentence.

◯ I can use a capital letter for place names, days of the week and months of the year.

◯ I can add –s or –es if there is more than one of something.

◯ I can put a question mark at the end of a question.

◯ I can add word endings to verbs and use them in sentences.

Section 3

◯ I can use an exclamation mark if it is needed.

◯ I can write three sentences with capital letters and full stops.

◯ I can use linking words like 'Then' and 'Next' to write about events in order.

◯ I can use describing words to add extra detail.

◯ I can add un– to words to change their meaning.